Mother Goose

Illustrated by
TONY BRICE

RAND McNALLY & COMPANY · CHICAGO

THERE WAS AN OLD WOMAN

There was an old woman who
    lived in a shoe.
She had so many children she
    didn't know what to do.
She gave them some broth with-
    out any bread.
She whipped them all soundly and
    put them to bed.

THE TARTS

The Queen of Hearts,
She made some tarts,
All on a summer's day;
The Knave of Hearts,
He stole the tarts,
And took them clean away.

The King of Hearts
Called for the tarts,
And beat the Knave full sore;
The Knave of Hearts
Brought back the tarts,
And vowed he'd steal no more.

LITTLE BO-PEEP

Little Bo-Peep has lost her sheep,
    And can't tell where to find
        them;
Leave them alone, and they'll
        come home,
    And bring their tails behind
        them.

MARY, MARY, QUITE
CONTRARY

Mary, Mary, quite contrary,
  How does your garden grow?
Silver bells and cockleshells,
  And pretty maids all of a row.

LITTLE BOY BLUE

Little Boy Blue, come, blow your
horn!
The sheep's in the meadow, the
cow's in the corn.
Where's the little boy that looks
after the sheep?
Under the haystack, fast asleep!

MISS MUFFET

Little Miss Muffet
Sat on a tuffet,
Eating of curds and whey;
There came a big spider,
And sat down beside her,
And frightened Miss Muffet away.

OLD MOTHER HUBBARD

Old Mother Hubbard
Went to the cupboard,
   To give her poor dog a bone;
But when she got there
The cupboard was bare,
   And so the poor dog had none.

RAIN

Rain, rain, go away,
Come again some other day;
Little Johnny wants to play.

BOBBY SHAFTOE

Bobby Shaftoe's gone to sea,
With silver buckles on his knee
He'll come back and marry me,
    Pretty Bobby Shaftoe!

Bobby Shaftoe's fat and fair,
Combing down his yellow hair;
He's my love for evermore,
    Pretty Bobby Shaftoe.

TOM, TOM, THE PIPER'S SON

Tom, Tom, the piper's son,
Stole a pig, and away he run.
The pig was eat,
And Tom was beat,
And Tom ran crying down the
street.

CURLY-LOCKS

Curly-locks, Curly-locks, wilt thou
    be mine?
Thou shalt not wash the dishes,
    nor yet feed the swine;
But sit on a cushion, and sew a
    fine seam,
And feed upon strawberries, sugar,
    and cream.

LITTLE TOM TUCKER

Little Tom Tucker
   Sings for his supper.
What shall he eat?
   White bread and butter.

How will he cut it
   Without e'er a knife?
How will he be married
   Without e'er a wife?

JACK SPRAT

Jack Sprat could eat no fat,
   His wife could eat no lean;
And so, betwixt them both,
   They licked the platter clean.

JACK AND JILL

Jack and Jill went up the hill,
To fetch a pail of water;
Jack fell down and broke his
crown,
And Jill came tumbling after.

Then up Jack got and off did trot,
  As fast as he could caper,
To old Dame Dob, who patched
    his nob
  With vinegar and brown paper.

LITTLE JACK HORNER

Little Jack Horner
Sat in the corner,
Eating of Christmas pie;
He put in his thumb,
And pulled out a plum,
And said, "What a good boy am I!"

THE PUMPKIN-EATER

Peter, Peter, pumpkin-eater,
Had a wife and couldn't keep her;
He put her in a pumpkin shell,
And there he kept her very well.

THIS LITTLE PIG

This little pig went to market;
This little pig stayed at home;
This little pig had roast beef;
This little pig had none;
This little pig said, "Wee, wee!
I can't find my way home."

HUMPTY DUMPTY

Humpty Dumpty sat on a wall,
Humpty Dumpty had a great fall;
And all the king's horses and all
   the king's men
Cannot put Humpty Dumpty
   together again.

PEASE PORRIDGE

Pease porridge hot,
    Pease porridge cold,
Pease porridge in the pot,
    Nine days old.

Some like it hot,
    Some like it cold,
Some like it in the pot,
    Nine days old.

HUSH-A-BYE

Hush-a-bye, baby, on the tree top
When the wind blows, the cradle
    will rock;

When the bough breaks, the cradle
    will fall;
Down will come baby, bough,
    cradle, and all.